CRITTERLAN

RAPID ROBERT ROADRUNNER

Story and pictures by Bob Reese

 CHILDRENS PRESS, CHICAGO

MY 30 WORDS ARE:

I	think	again
am	that	hop
feel	should	is
bad	will	fun
rest	to	but
make	the	come
me	sand	we
sad	cactus	hide
run	and	sandy
good	back	when

Library of Congress Cataloging in Publication Data
Reese, Bob.
   Rapid Robert Roadrunner.
   (Critterland adventures)
   Summary: Rapid Robert explains why he loves to
run through the desert.
   [1.   Road runner (Bird)—Fiction.   2.   Running—
Fiction.   3.   Stories in rhyme]   I.   Title.
II.   Series.
PZ8.3.R255Rap   [E]   81-6090
ISBN 0-516-02305-5   AACR2

I am feeling bad.

Resting makes me sad.

Running feels good.

I think that I should.

I will run to the sandy sand,

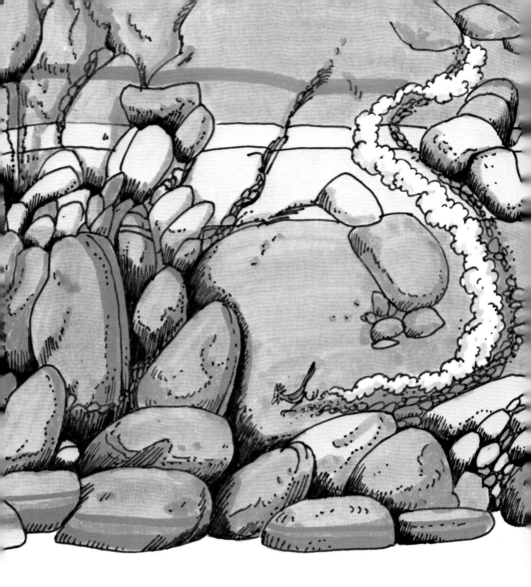

to the cactus and back again.

Hopping is fun,
but come and run.

We will run to the sandy sand,
to the cactus and back again.

Hiding is fun,
but come and run.

We will run to the sandy sand,
to the cactus and back again.

Thinking is fun,
but come and run.

We will run to the sandy sand,
to the cactus and back again.

Resting is fun.

Hopping is fun.

Hiding is fun.

Thinking is fun.

But when I am feeling bad,
and when I am feeling sad,

I run to the sandy sand,
to the cactus and back again.

Bob Reese was born in 1938 in Hollywood, California. His mother Isabelle was an English teacher in the Los Angeles City Schools.

After his graduation from high school he went to work for Walt Disney Studios as an animation cartoonist. He received his B.S. degree in Art and Business and began work as a freelance illustrator and designer.

He currently resides in the mountains of Utah with his wife Nancy and daughters Natalie and Brittany.